It's only you that's incompatibl

Mel Calman

It's only you that's incompatible!

MANDARIN

IT'S ONLY YOU THAT'S INCOMPATIBLE!

First published in 1984 by Methuen London Ltd

This edition published in 1991 by Mandarin Paperbacks
Michelin House, 81 Fulham Road, London SW3 6RB

Mandarin is an imprint of the Octopus Group

Copyright © Mel Calman 1984
Designed by Philip Thompson
ISBN: 0 7493 0820 6
A CIP catalogue record for this book is available
from the British Library

Printed in England by Clays Ltd, St Ives plc

To 'Red shoes'...

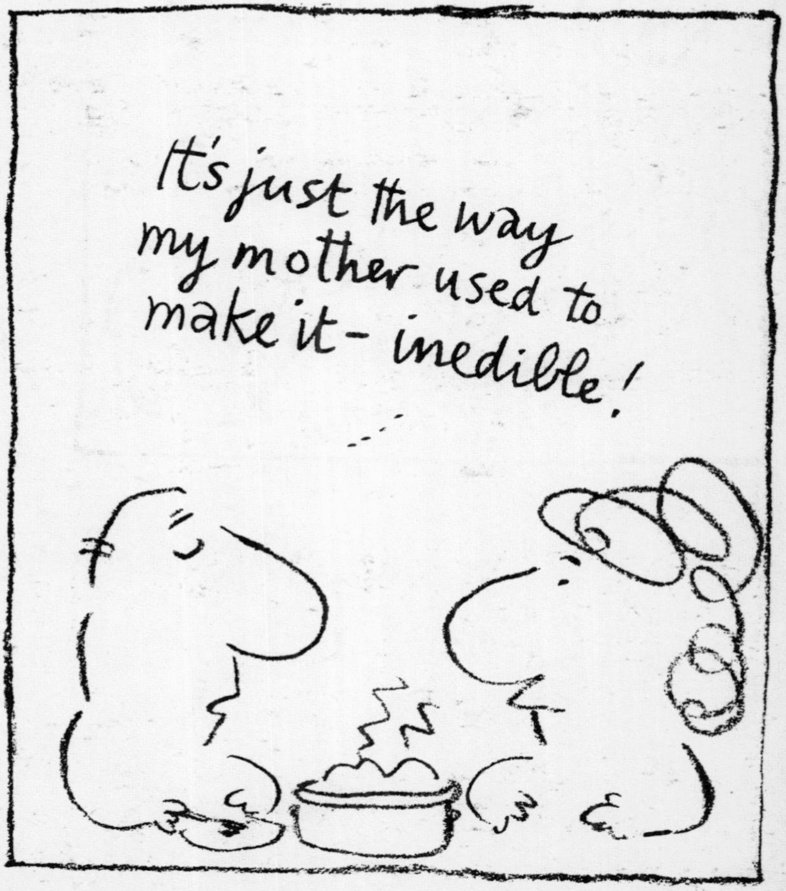
It's just the way my mother used to make it - inedible!

In a minute SHE will
phone – as promised –
and we will TALK
and renew our
lines of
communication.

LATER
SILENCE! She must be ILL - or have FORGOTTEN! IMPOSSIBLE!
Dont LOOK at me like that - it's not my FAULT..

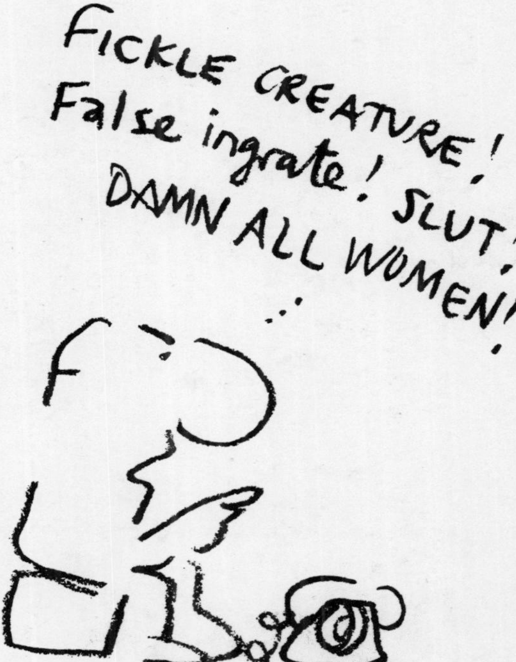
FICKLE CREATURE!
False ingrate! SLUT!
DAMN ALL WOMEN!

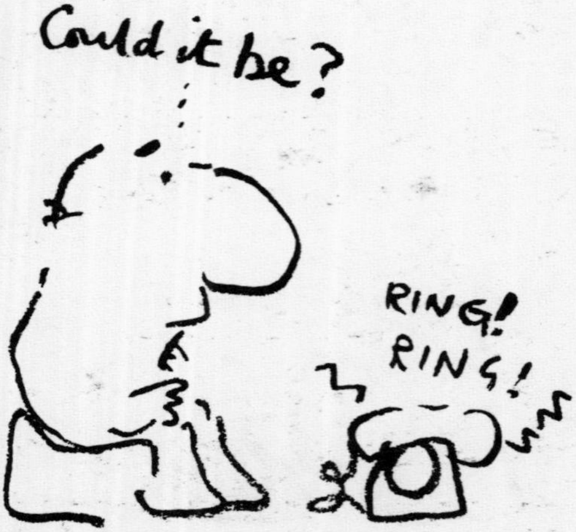
Could it be?
RING!
RING!

HOW NICE!
Fancy you phoning —
I'd quite forgotten you
said you
WOULD!

They are OUT eating 'sole bonne femme' and I've got OLD fish heads..

Why is the plat du jour always FISH?
FOOD

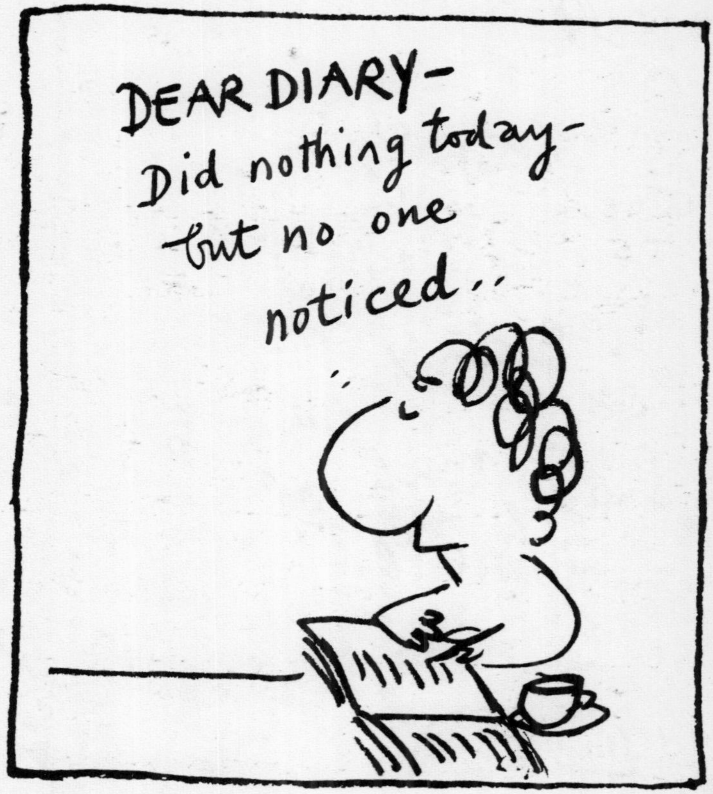
DEAR DIARY-
Did nothing today-
but no one
noticed..

I will LOVE you
forever and
forever – so long
as we don't have to
see so much of
each other...

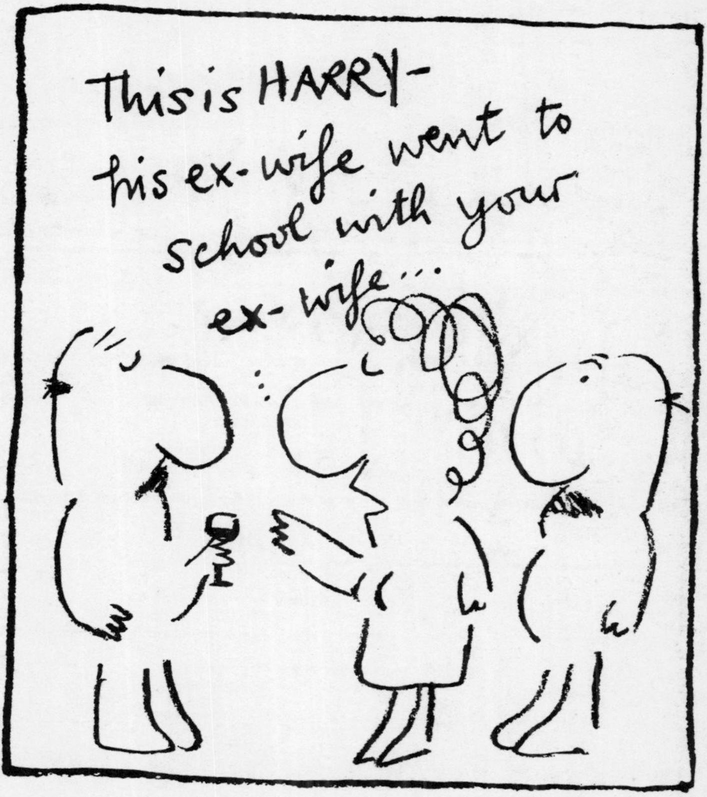
This is HARRY-
his ex-wife went to
school with your
ex-wife...

Look- there's lovely
Franklin Pangborn and...
quick.. that's Una Merkel-
you know, the one you always
confuse with Zasu Pitts. She
was in that Stroheim movie
(NO. NOT Merkel- PITTS).. Isn't that
Charlie Ruggles.. he's the one you
thought was Charles Laughton..
Remember they were in that movie
we saw last Christmas- where
Edward Arnold or do I mean
Eugene
Palette?
Anyway...

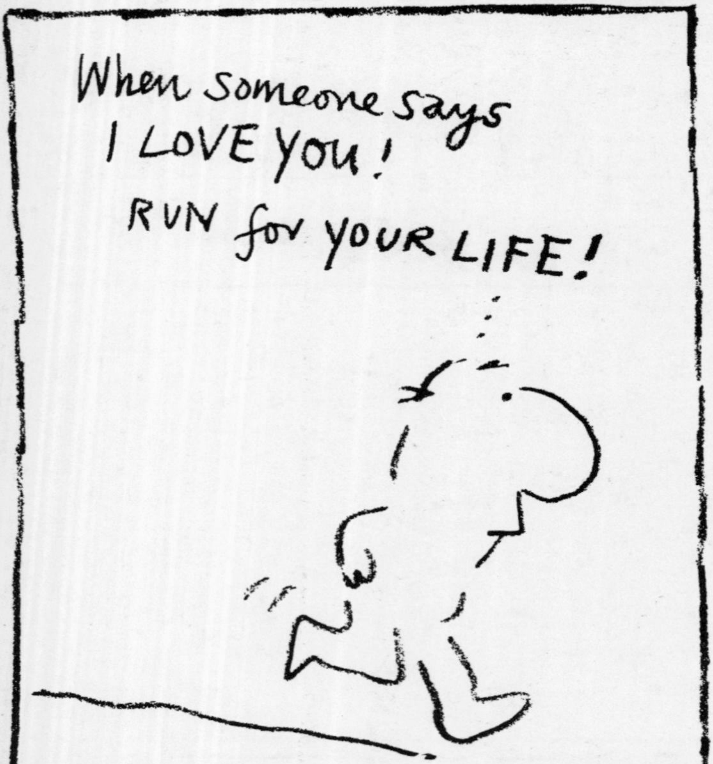
When someone says
I LOVE YOU!
RUN for YOUR LIFE!

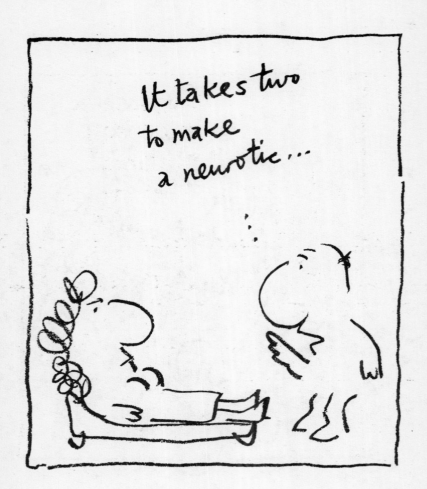

You're so OLD
that girl wasn't even
offended when
you leered at her...

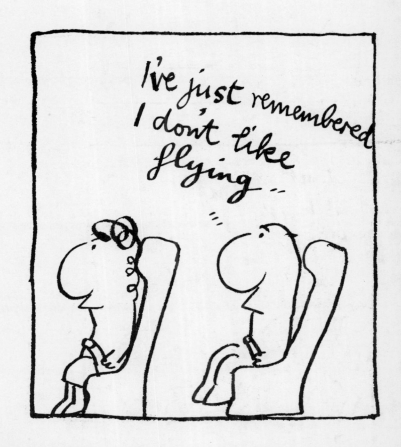

she NEVER rings me!

He never rings me...

I think that I think
too much – I really
should do LESS thinking –
If only I could STOP
ALL THIS THINKING, I'd be
so much happier –
(I think)

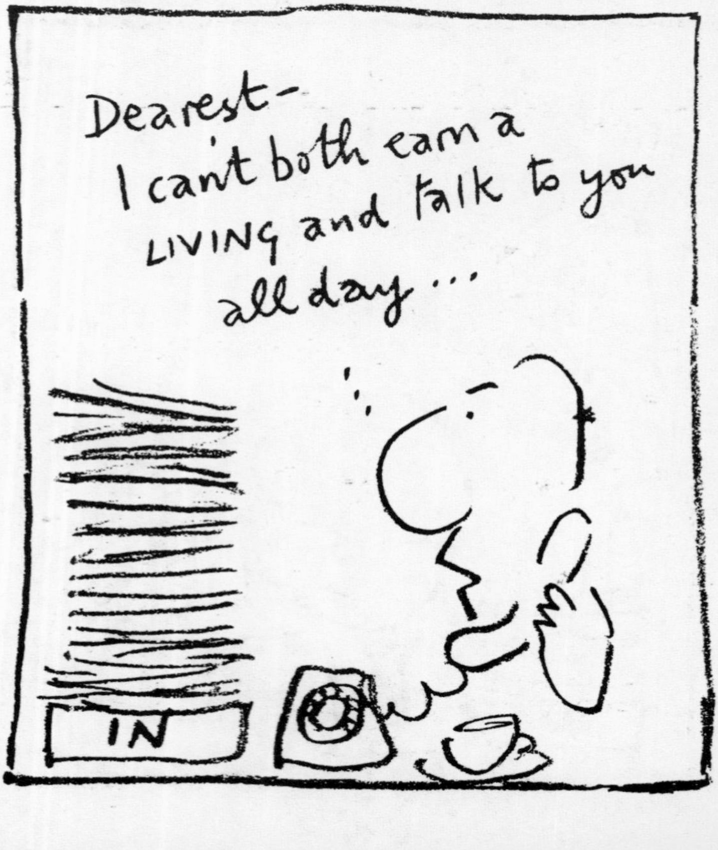
Dearest-
I can't both earn a LIVING and talk to you all day ...
IN

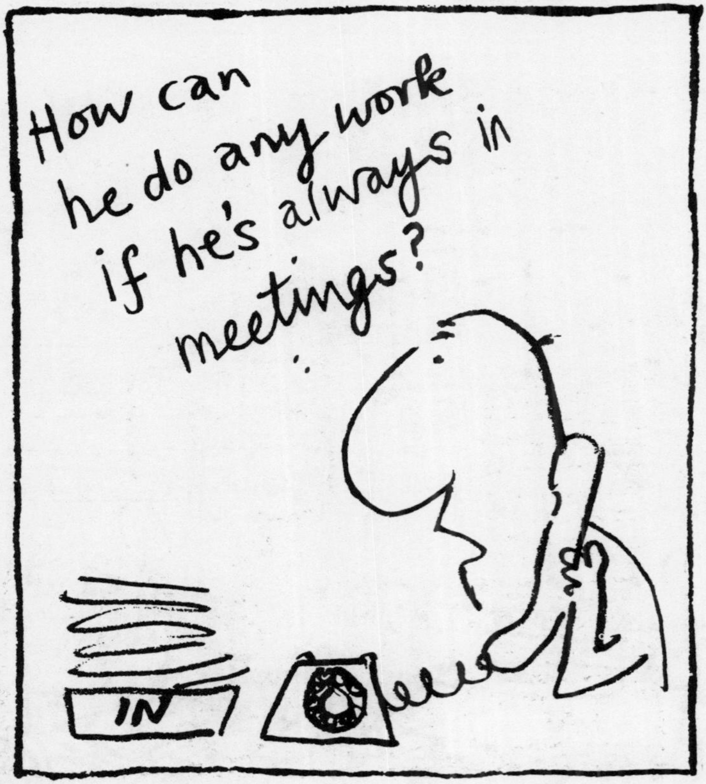
How can he do any work if he's always in meetings?
IN

Does this mean
You're leaving?

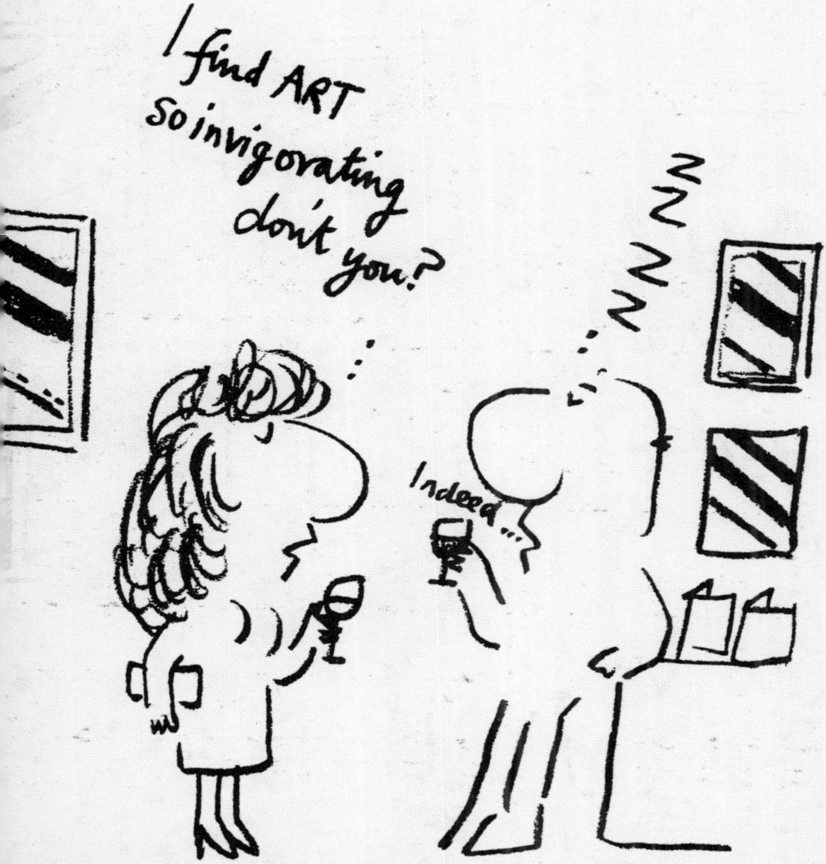
I find ART so invigorating don't you?
Indeed...
ZZZZ

What do you REALLY want?
I want you to know without my telling you..

All you think about is SEX, SEX, SEX, SEX..
But I only bought these to PLEASE you...
How to ENJOY SEX
The Joy of SEX
What is AN ORGASM?
The ART of FOREPLAY

Why should I phone him?
I ALWAYS phone him..
And he's probably not in..
ALWAYS OUT doing things-
enjoying himself..
He never phones me.
I wish he would just
ONCE phone me..
I'll give him five more
minutes, and then
I'm going out!

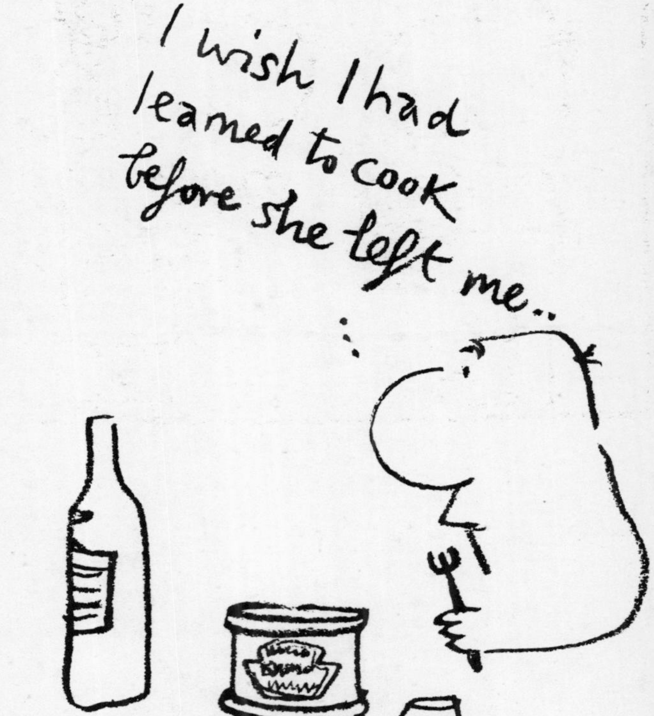
I wish I had learned to cook before she left me..
FROZEN COD

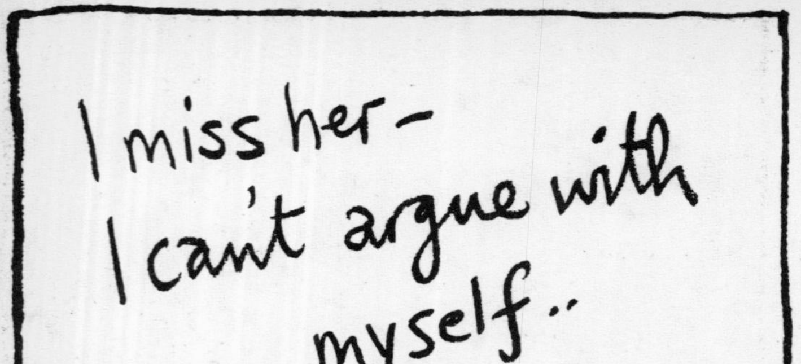
I miss her-
I can't argue with
myself..
NEWS

My SEX LIFE is more 'Interruptus' than 'coitus'..

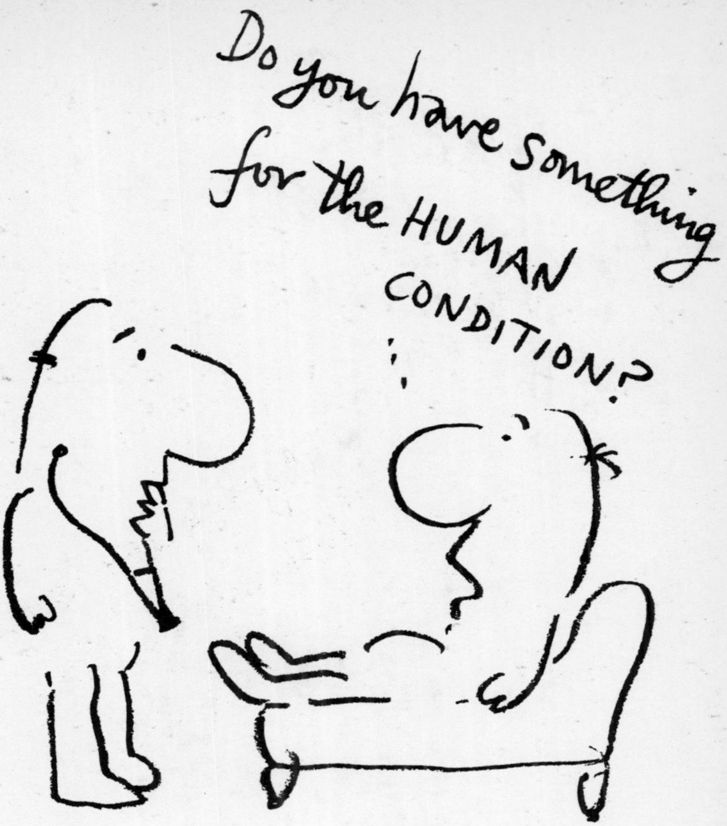
Do you have something for the HUMAN CONDITION?

I hated the play
but I loved the
way you kicked
that man to get
to the bar...

When WOMEN say you need a better Woman – it means they've found a BETTER man...

Should I ask her for her 'phone number NOW – or WAIT a BIT?
If he doesn't ask me for my 'phone number soon – I'M LEAVING...
Lovely Party!

I LOVE you –
because you remind
me of ME...

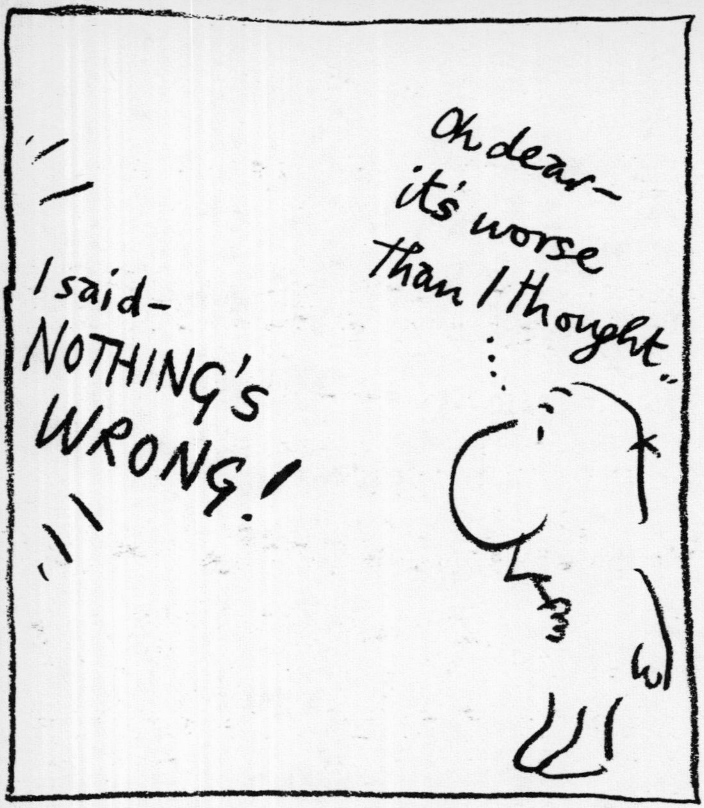
I said- NOTHING'S WRONG!
Oh dear- it's worse than I thought...

I've discovered what
WOMEN want —
It's what they
didn't want
yesterday...

Will you be able to support a second wife in the style to which your first wife is accustomed?

I'm bored in BED
because I'm not
my
type...

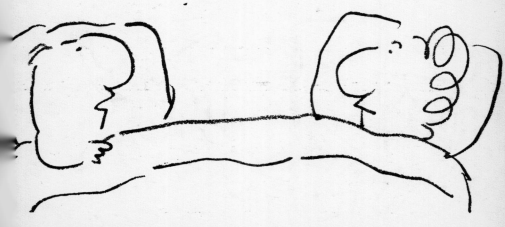

How nice a winter's life
would be - without
the writing...

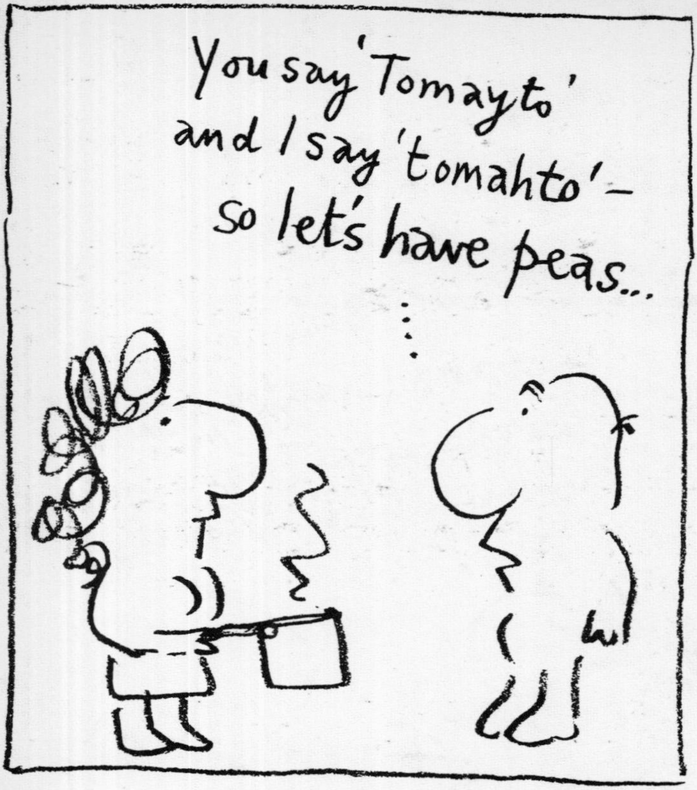
You say 'Tomayto'
and I say 'tomahto' –
so let's have peas...

My horoscope today
said I'd meet a man
interested in my
feet...

You say your PILLOW
is 100% PURE DOWN—
but I say it is 80%
PURE DOWN and
20% Polyester granules..

PILLOW TALK

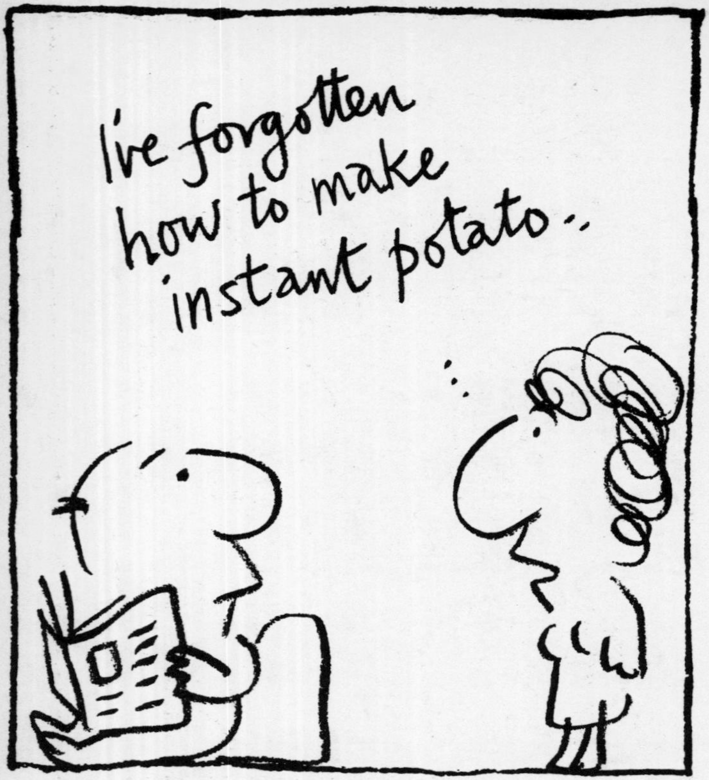
I've forgotten how to make instant potato..

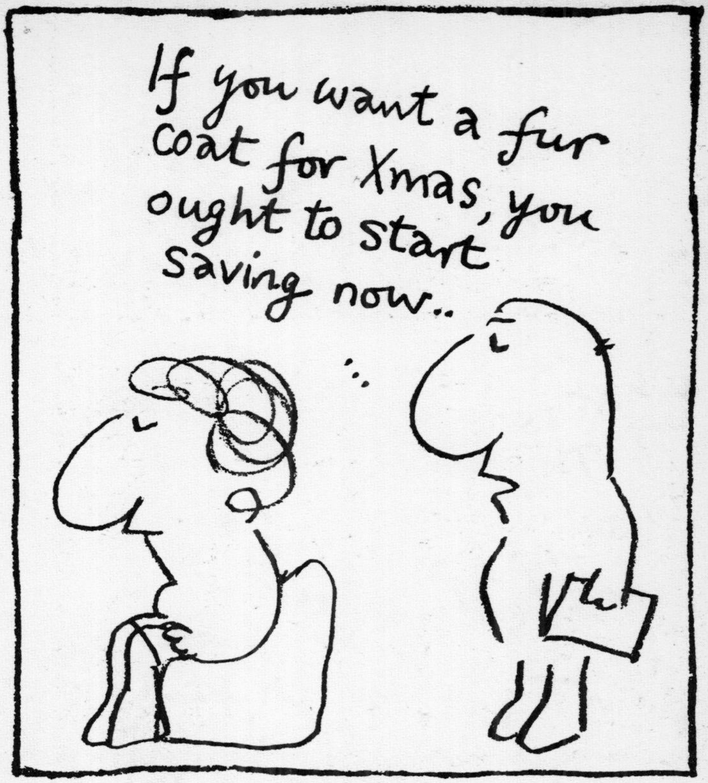
If you want a fur coat for Xmas, you ought to start saving now..
...

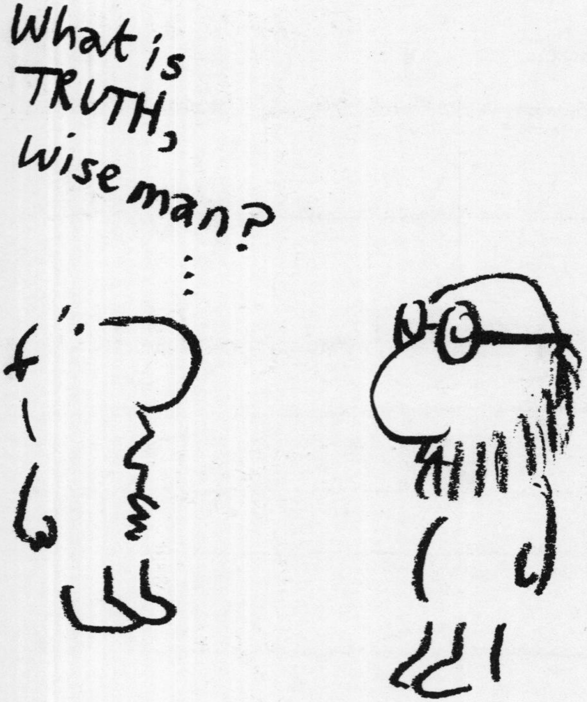
What is TRUTH, wise man?

TRUTH is too
precious to tell
every FOOL who
asks for it ..

My WIFE hasn't spoken to me for three days...
Perhaps she's trying to tell you something...